Lions at Last

by Andrew Whitmore
illustrated by Brad Quinn

W9-AWC-985

Table of Contents

Chapter I
The Mighty Lions?

Soccer wasn't just a game to Carlos.
It was his whole life.

His father worked among the vendors at the local soccer ground. He owned a little stall that sold meat empanadas and fresh fruit juices. Carlos went along with him every Saturday to watch the village team play.

Carlos and his friends practiced before and after school every day. On the weekends they played games against neighboring villages.

Their team was called the Mighty Lions. But they hadn't been too mighty lately. In fact, they had lost every game so far this season.

Paulo was the best player on their team. He dreamed of being a Brazilian soccer star, like Pelé and Ronaldo.

"I'm going to score 1,000 goals," he said. "And help Brazil add another three World Cups to its collection!"

Carlos would be happy to score just one goal. Or win just one game, especially a game against the Wolves.

The Wolves won every game against the Mighty Lions. The team's players were always making fun of Carlos and his friends.

"Some Lions you are," their captain would say. "You should call yourselves the Kittens!"

Chapter 2
A New Player

One day Carlos and Paulo arrived at training to find their coach smiling from ear to ear.

"We have a new player on the team," their coach told them. He pointed to a small figure already out on the soccer field. "Her name is Susana."

"Is she any good?" asked Paulo.

The coach's smile got even bigger. "Just wait and see," he said.

Susana was amazing. She was as quick and alert as a cat.

Susana could do all kinds of tricks with the ball. She could even bounce it from one shoulder to the other and juggle it with her feet.

Susana could kick the ball so hard, the goalposts almost fell down!

Carlos couldn't wait for the weekend. His team was playing the Wolves again. This time the Mighty Lions had a big surprise.

Everyone was really excited before the match.
But Paulo was not happy.

Susana had taken over as the team's number
one goal shooter. He would have to play in
the back line with Carlos now.

"It's not fair," said Paulo. "I'm just as good at kicking goals as she is."

"Don't worry about it," said Carlos. "Right now we have to stop the Wolves from kicking more goals than we do."

The referee blew his whistle, and the game started.

Having Susana on the team made a big difference. Everyone seemed to play much better to keep up with her.

At half time the score was still 0–0. The coach of the Mighty Lions was very proud of his team.

"Keep it up, kids!" he exclaimed. "You're sure doing a great job!"

Carlos's team battled hard all the way through the second half.

Susana almost scored, but the ball was stopped by the goalie. It looked as if the game was going to end with no winner.

Then just as the final whistle was about to blow, the Wolves' captain tripped Susana. The referee gave the Lions a free kick!

Chapter 3
The Lions Roar

Susana got up limping. There was a look of concern on her face. She rubbed her ankle for a while, and then waved to Paulo.

"Don't just stand there," Carlos told Paulo. "See what she wants."

Susana whispered something to Paulo. He nodded and moved to one side.

The Wolves lined up in front of Susana to block her kick. She would have to fire the ball right through them to score a goal.

Susana didn't even try. Instead she kicked the ball straight over their heads. Paulo ran in and slammed it into the back of the net. Goal!

Everyone was cheering so loudly they almost didn't hear the final whistle blow.

Carlos ran over to Paulo and slapped him on the back.

"You did it!" shouted Carlos. "You won the game!"

"No," said Paulo, looking at Susana. "We did it."

Carlos and his teammates had a big celebration. Carlos's father provided empanadas and cold juice for everyone.

The Wolves came over to say good-bye.

"I guess you're not kittens after all," said the Wolves' captain.

Carlos smiled.

They certainly weren't. They were true lions at last.

Comprehension Check

Retell the Story

Use a Character and Setting Chart and the pictures to help you retell this story.

Characters	Setting

Think and Compare

1. Turn to page 7. What special tricks can Susana do with a soccer ball? What does that tell you about her? *(Analyze Character and Setting)*

2. What position do you or would you like to play on a soccer team? Explain. *(Apply)*

3. Why do you think soccer is one of the most popular games in the world? *(Analyze)*